Buttons

Put on 5 .
Take away 4.

How many
are left? ☐

Put on 6 .
Take away 1.

How many
are left? ☐

4 take away 3 = ☐

5 take away 2 = ☐

8 take away 4 = ☐

6 take away 4 = ☐

7 take away 3 = ☐

9 take away 5 = ☐

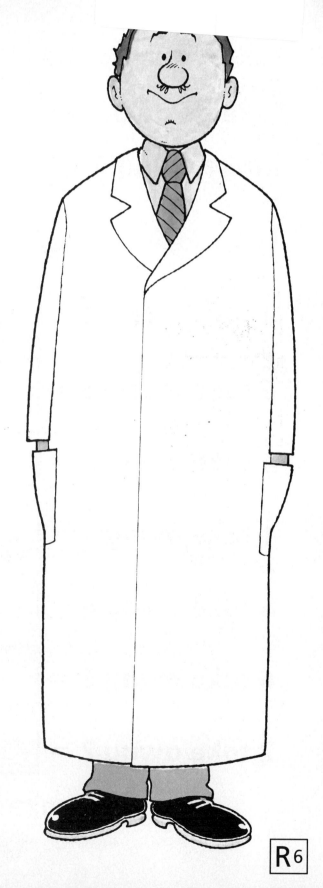

R 6

Blast off!

Put 5 in the rocket.

Take away 5.

5 take away 5 = ☐

3 take away 3 = ☐

6 take away 6 = ☐

4 take away 3 = ☐

I take away I = ☐

4 take away 4 = ☐

6 take away 5 = ☐

2 take away 2 = ☐

I

Cars

Put on 4 cars.
Take away 1.

How many are left? ☐

Put on 5 cars.
Take away 3.

How many are left? ☐

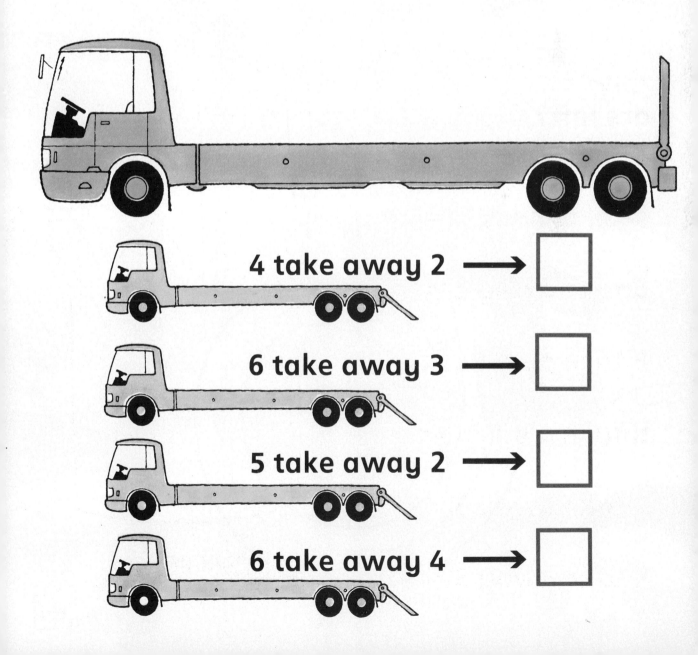

4 take away 2 ⟶ ☐

6 take away 3 ⟶ ☐

5 take away 2 ⟶ ☐

6 take away 4 ⟶ ☐

SPMG

HEINEMANN MATHEMATICS 1

Name

WORKBOOK 6
Subtraction to 6

Revised

Spots

Put on 6 spots.   Take away 3.

$6 - 3 = \boxed{}$

6 take away 5.

$6 - 5 = \boxed{}$

5 take away 1.

$5 - 1 = \boxed{}$

7 take away 4.

$7 - 4 = \boxed{}$

8 take away 3.

$8 - 3 = \boxed{}$

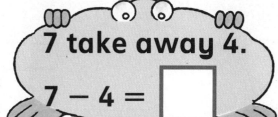

$3 - 2 = \boxed{}$ $6 - 3 = \boxed{}$

10 Plates

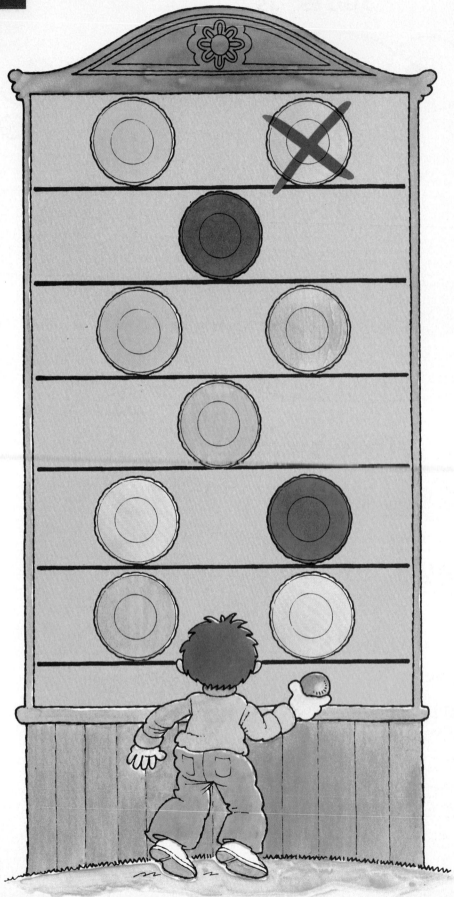

$10 - 1 = \boxed{9}$

$9 - 1 = \boxed{}$

$8 - 1 = \boxed{}$

$7 - 1 = \boxed{}$

$6 - 1 = \boxed{}$

$5 - 1 = \boxed{}$

$4 - 1 = \boxed{}$

$3 - 1 = \boxed{}$

$2 - 1 = \boxed{}$

$1 - 1 = \boxed{}$

Fried eggs

10 eggs.

Eat 2 eggs.

10 − 2 = ☐

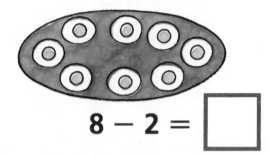

8 − 2 = ☐

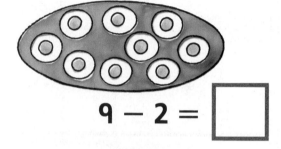

9 − 2 = ☐

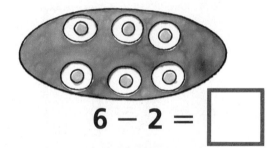

6 − 2 = ☐

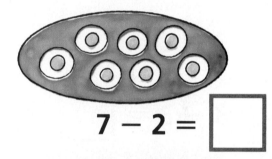

7 − 2 = ☐

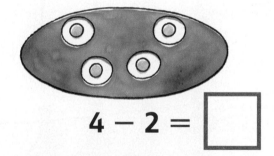

4 − 2 = ☐

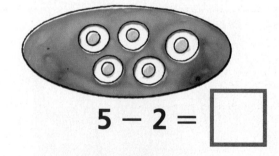

5 − 2 = ☐

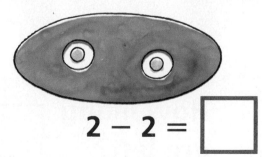

2 − 2 = ☐

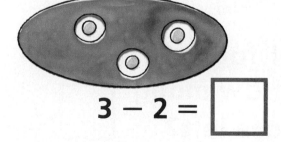

3 − 2 = ☐

Flying

How many planes? ☐

How many birds? ☐

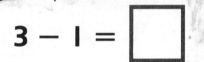

3 − 1 = ☐

3 − 2 = ☐

3 − 3 = ☐

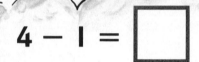

4 − 1 = ☐

4 − 2 = ☐

4 − 3 = ☐

4 − 4 = ☐

1 falls off. How many are left? ☐

2 fall off. How many are left? ☐

The pond

How many ducks in the pond? □

Hide I duck. $5 - 1 =$ □

$5 - 2 =$ □

$5 - 3 =$ □

$5 - 4 =$ □

$5 - 5 =$ □

$5 - 4 =$ □ $4 - 3 =$ □

$5 - 5 =$ □ $5 - 3 =$ □

2 swans fly away.

How many are left? □

Bubbles

$6 - 1 =$ ☐

$6 - 2 =$ ☐

$6 - 3 =$ ☐

$6 - 4 =$ ☐

$6 - 5 =$ ☐

$6 - 4 =$ ☐

$6 - 2 =$ ☐

$6 - 6 =$ ☐

$6 - 1 =$ ☐

$6 - 5 =$ ☐

11

Pet shop

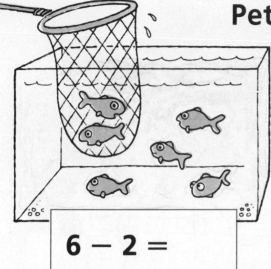

6 − 2 =

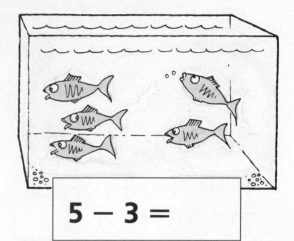

5 − 3 =

3 − 1 =

4 − 3 =

6 − 3 =

2 − 2 =

4 − 1 =

Pet shop

How many are left? ☐

How many are left? ☐

How many are left? ☐

How many are left? ☐

How many are left? ☐

How many are left? ☐

3 get out.

How many are left? ☐

R9

Jumble sale

Each has 6p to spend.

How much is left? ☐ p

How much is left? ☐ p

How much is left? ☐ p

How much is left? ☐ p

How much is left? ☐ p

How much is left? ☐ p

Match

Make 2.

Make 3.

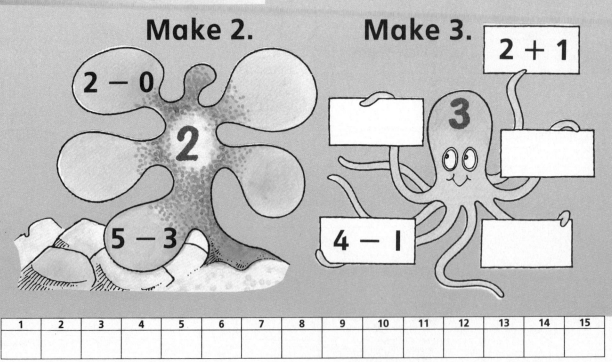

1	2	3	4	5	6	7	8	9	10	11	12	13	14	15

Published by Heinemann Educational Publishers, Halley Court, Jordan Hill, Oxford OX2 8EJ,
a division of Reed Educational and Professional Publishers Ltd.
ISBN 0 435 03706 4 © Scottish Primary Mathematics Group 1991.
First published 1991. Revised edition 1995.   96 97 98 99   7 6 5 4 3 2
Typeset and Illustrated by Oxprint Design. Printed by Jarrold Printing, Norwich.

ISBN 0-435-03087-6